PET POEMS

How to write poems about pets
(also not just pets)

Watch our **Intro video** at
www.PetPoemsPlus.com!

Whenever you see this red
symbol, there's a **VIDEO**
to watch! All videos are at
www.PetPoemsPlus.com.
Make sure you have adult
permission before watching.

by Typewriter Rodeo's
Sean Petrie
&
Amanda Hoxworth
&
YOU

My favorite animal:

Pets I have:

Pet I want someday:

This book in your hands

Is more of a **PLAY**book than a WORKbook.

Because creating things should be **FUN**.

This other book ↓

PET POEMS
(also not just pets)

I WON AN AWARD!

poems by Sean Petrie

art by Amanda Hoxworth

has **examples** of what we'll create.

But if you don't have it, don't worry --
we'll give you everything you need in these pages.

And who are we?

we are

HELLO
My Name Is
Sean!

HELLO
My Name Is
Amanda!

We're the authors of the award-winning poetry book,
PET POEMS (also not just pets).

Sean has also written a bunch of other books. And over
20,000 poems, most on a typewriter!

Amanda is also a professional artist. She's made lots
of art, most by throwing paint on paper!

But, we're not the **ONLY** authors here --

the authors!

YOU are an author too!

HELLO
My Name Is

Please write your name here

Yes, you can write in here – it's your book!

Please put a picture of yourself in the box above -- draw, tape a photo, put a smiley face, do whatever you want!

Excellent! Now, **the THREE of us** (go, Team Authors!) are all set to create cool stuff about pets (also not just pets)...

READY??

1. Name this Owl

chapter video

All chapter videos are at
PetPoemsPlus.com

Please look at this owl.

Not just a quick glance --
STUDY it.

Now, what NAME
do you think it wants to go by?

Maybe it wants a name like Nick or Esme.
Or something like Wind or Happy.

Please write the name you think it wants over here.
There is no wrong name.

2

HELLO
My Name Is
Griffin Sky

Now, imagine this owl is flying towards something.

Maybe it's headed towards home, or food, or its owly friends, or something else. **There is no wrong thing the owl is flying towards.**

Please draw what it's flying towards, in this box:

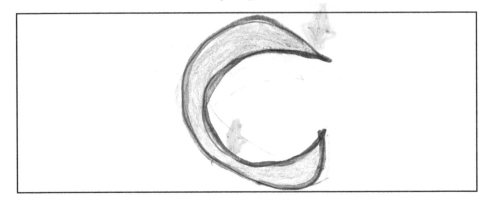

Awesome! You just gave this owl a **mission**!

In the oval below, please write its name again.

In the box under it, please write what the owl would say to finish each line if it could talk. For example, what would it say it's flying towards?

You might study the owl and your drawing on the other page to help. **There are no wrong things the owl would say.**

owl's name

Griffin Sky

what the owl would say

I am flying towards

the moon

I am faster than

the moon

In my dreams, I can

Shape Shift

When you're done, turn the page —

Hello, POET!!

What you just wrote?

IT'S A POEM.

Just like music only needs **sounds**,
a poem only needs **words**.

It doesn't have to rhyme or be about love.
It doesn't even have to make sense!

That's one of the blissful things about poems:

THERE. ARE. NO. RULES.

In poetry, you can be a rebel.

But, if there are no poetry rules --

What makes a **good** poem?

Well, it seems to help if you **really look at** what the poem is about. Like you did with your owl poem!

I'M REALLY LOOKING!

That's what Sean did to help with the poem below from *Pet Poems*.

First, Amanda painted this dog. (Hi, dog!)

Then Sean **looked** at it a while ... and named it Thimble. (Hi, Thimble!)

Then Sean **imagined** what Thimble would say if it could talk...

Thimble

I am tiny
But full of power!
I can run in circles
For one full hour!

That's an IMAGINE poem.
It imagines what an animal would say
if it could talk.

You've already written an IMAGINE poem!
That's what your owl poem was.

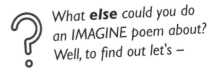

What **else** could you do
an IMAGINE poem about?
Well, to find out let's –

7

2. Pick-a-Pet!

chapter video

Please look at the dog and cat on the next page.

Which would you most want as a pet?

Ok, now <u>rip that one out</u> of the book.

Yes, for real!

Go ahead -- rip along that dotted line across the middle, then rip up or down to tear out the dog or cat.

Remember, **this is your book!**

You are one of its authors!

Please -- rip rip rip!

PS: Don't worry if you mess up!

There are extra Pick-a-Pet pages
at the back of this book
and at <u>PetPoemsPlus.com</u>.

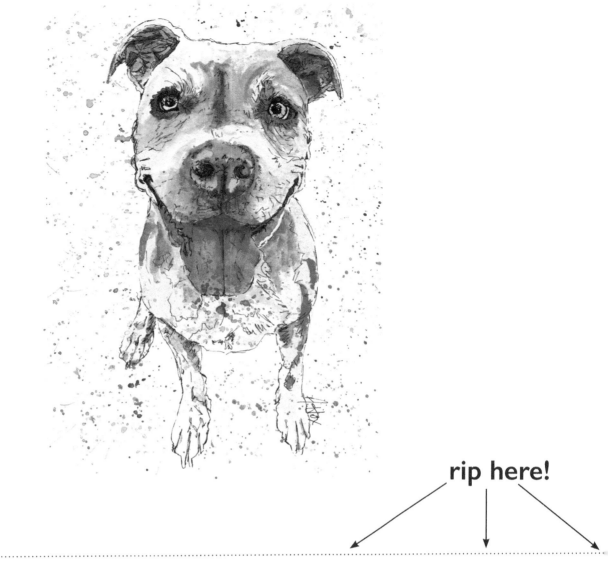

rip here!

Hello!
I'm the page on the other side
of the **dog!**

- -

Hello!
I'm the page on the other side
of the **cat!**

Done? Great!

Please turn the page, and
take your **new pet** with you!

3. Artist Monocle

chapter video

STOP

Before we do anything else,
you need your Artist Monocle!

What is an **Artist Monocle?**

It helps you see things like **ONLY YOU** can.

No two people will draw a dog the exact same way
or write the same poem about a cat's crummy day.

That's because everyone has a unique view
of the world -- through their **Artist Monocle.**

Let's make
yours!

ARTIST MONOCLE INSTRUCTIONS

Step 1: More ripping! **Rip out** the bottom half of this page.

Step 2: **Carefully cut** around the dashed lines.
When you use scissors, make sure an adult is around.
Make a hole in the gray center part.
<u>Hint:</u> Poking the center with a pencil might help.

Step 3: **Decorate** your Monocle! Use markers, stickers, whatever!

rip here

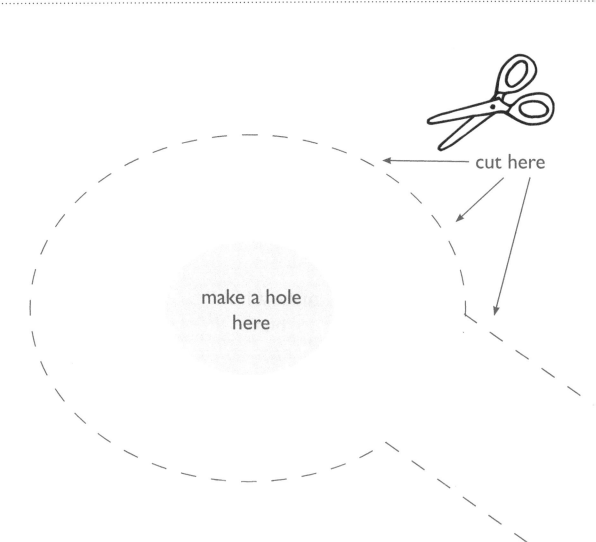

make a hole
here

cut here

Don't worry if you mess up!

There are extra Monocle-making pages
at the back of this book
and at PetPoemsPlus.com.

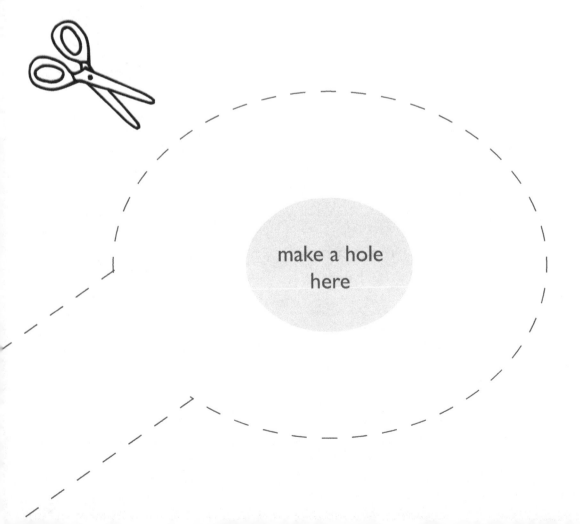

make a hole
here

Below is what Sean did for his Artist Monocle -- decorate yours however YOU want!

When yours is done, please take your new **dog or cat pet** and your **Artist Monocle** and turn the page!

Please hold your Artist Monocle up to your **eye**.

Look at your new pet **through** it for 10 seconds.

Now, what name do you think your pet wants?

Please 𝔴𝔯𝔦𝔱𝔢
its name here:

There are no wrong names.

Now, please look at your pet through your Artist Monocle
for 10 more seconds and --

figure out a **secret** your pet has,
that only you know.

Got its secret? Excellent! Now let's --

Introduce your pet!

Please **write** about your pet below.

(Use your Artist Monocle to help.)

 your pet's name

what would your pet say?

You think you know me, but here is my secret:

_____

When I am excited, this is what I SHOUT:

_____

When I am sad, this is what I whisper:

_____

down here, please write or <u>draw</u> something else about your pet!

When you're done, turn the page and do a —

POETRY LEAP!!

Get up and do it!

Leap!
Kick out!
Raise your arms!
Because --

YOU HAVE WRITTEN TWO IMAGINE POEMS!

You wrote one **IMAGINE** poem about the owl and another about the dog or cat!

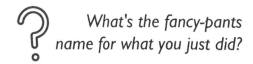

What's the fancy-pants name for what you just did?

There are
actually **TWO!**

Personification

/ per-son-i-fi-ca-tion /

making an animal act like a person

A dog can't really say its name.
But in a poem it can!

> HELLO, MY
> NAME IS BINGLY.

In a poem, a dog can say its name, drive
a truck, or do anything a **person** can!

> WOULD YOU
> LIKE ME TO
> DRIVE?

That's personification.

Some folks also call it **anthropomorphism**, but we'll
stick with personification. (It's shorter!) And whatever you
call it, it can make your poem **sparkle**!

So can –

Ekphrasis

/ ek-phra-sis /

writing about a work of art

Remember when you looked at this painting, and then wrote about the owl?

THANKS FOR TELLING MY STORY!

That was ekphrasis. You can do it with a painting, drawing, sculpture, or any work of art.

Now you have **two kinds** of poetry sparkle, from your IMAGINE poems!

Are IMAGINE poems the **only** kind?

Not even!

Here's another kind of poem --

Sloth Secrets

Well hello there, slothy
With your extra-long toe
Why oh why, slothy
Are you so   s   l   o   w?

That's a **QUESTION** poem.
It asks an animal a question.

22

That sloth **QUESTION** poem could end there.

Or it could keep going and --

- give an answer
- ask the sloth more questions
- do anything else!

Remember, in poetry --

There are no rules.

Hello.
Please get your
Artist Monocle so we can –

4. Ask-a-Cat!

chapter video

Please pick one of the cats below.

Now, please look at the cat through your Artist Monocle.

If that cat could answer you, what **two questions** would you ask it?

Please **write** your two questions on the next page, beneath the two we came up with.

There are no wrong cat questions.

24

Who do you dream about, cat?

What does happiness smell like, cat?

_____

_____

our 2 cat
questions

your 2 cat
questions

aaaaand ... BOOM!

YOU JUST WROTE A QUESTION POEM!

Does a QUESTION poem need **answers**?

Not at all!

But it can if you want! If you have ideas for what
the cat might say, you can write its answers above.
(You can put them beneath each question.)

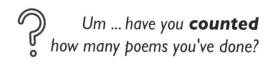

_Um ... have you **counted**
how many poems you've done?_   25

You've written at least 2 **IMAGINE** poems.

You've written at least 1 **QUESTION** poem.

That means you've already done **at least 3 poems.**

Snack time!

You've earned a **poetry cupcake!**

(caution: not a real cupcake)

> If you like **IMAGINE** poems, check out:
> - *Dog Songs* by Mary Oliver
> - *At the Library* by Nikki Grimes

> If you like **QUESTION** poems, check out:
> - *The Toucan* by Shel Silverstein
> - *One Boy Told Me* by Naomi Shihab Nye

As we're enjoying our snacks -- **do you have a pet** at home?

If so, please 𝕨𝕣𝕚𝕥𝕖 its name below. If you have lots, pick one. You could also put the name of a pet you used to have.

If you don't have a pet, think of a pet you'd like to have, and come up with a name for it.

Now, please 𝕨𝕣𝕚𝕥𝕖 a QUESTION or IMAGINE poem about that pet.

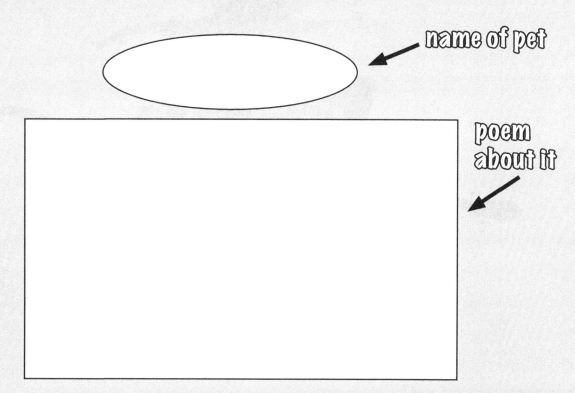

name of pet

poem about it

You've now done **FOUR POEMS!!!** *That deserves more than a poetry cupcake. Let's have a —*

POETRY DANCE PARTY!

dance party! video

DANCE PARTY INSTRUCTIONS

1. Put down your pen or pencil.

2. Put on your **favorite song.**

3. Get up and --

4. Dance!!!!

Celebrate!

SMILE!

Snap!

Shake it!

Spinnnn!

5. Poem-Formance

Whew, that was fun!
But **don't sit down yet.** Let's do a --

What's a poem-formance?

It's reading a poem out loud.

When poets publish a new book, they often read from it at a book release party.

Let's pretend you just published a book of poems and --

hold up --

we don't have to pretend -- you have poems in this book!

Please pick one of your poems in this book.

Got one? Great! Now let's practice --

How **NOT** to do a Poem-Formance.

chapter video

 Read your poem's **first line** out loud LIKE A ROBOT. Try not to move your body at all.

Now, do the opposite -- read that line with EMOTION. Make us **FEEL** the poem!! Yes, great!

Okay, read the next line so softly that no one can hear you.

Now, do the opposite -- belt it out **LOUD** and **PROUD**! Yes, like that!!

Finally, read the next line so **FAST** that your words blur together like a racing cheetah!

Now, do the opposite -- read it **SLOWLY** enough so that we can all follow along. Yes, perfect -- thank you!

Now you're ready to —

31

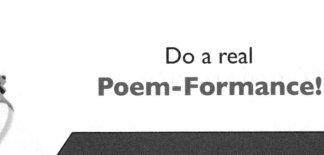

Do a real
Poem-Formance!

1. Raise your shoulders.

2. Do your best superhero stance.

3. Imagine your words are golden, flowing magic.

4. Say, "Ba ba ba BOOM!" Feel the power of your voice.

5. Take a deep breath, and --

READ YOUR POEM!

*Remember -- read with **emotion**, and be **loud** and **slow** enough that we can all follow along.*

How did that feel?

If you want, do it again!

Try doing a Poem-Formance
with a friend ⟶

Is your poem happy or funny?
Try **smiling** when you read it.

Is your poem sad?
Try **pausing** between lines.

Does your poem have action?
Gesture. **Act it out.**

Most of all, BE THE POEM.
Feel it in your bones, read it like no one else can.

Watch our Poem-Formances
at www.PetPoemsPlus.com!

Ball is ALL

If you want, send us your Poem-Formance!
(Get permission first!)
Send to: videos@petpoemsbook.com

Now it's time to –

33

6. Forge Your Poetry Sword!

TO FORGE YE OLDE POETRY SWORD:

1. Find a pencil, pen, or small stick.
2. Wrap it with aluminum foil.
3. Decorate!

sword-making tips:
PetPoemsPlus.com

Keep your **Poetry Sword** in a trusty place. (Sean's is on his desk.) ⟶

HI, I'M SEAN'S POETRY SWORD.

When you're feeling stuck, pick up the sword, feel its power -- **YOUR** power.

To slay fear. To create **anything** you want. And to --

7. Break-a-Line!

chapter video

In a story, each line **ends at the edge** of the paper, then a new line starts. Like this:

STORY

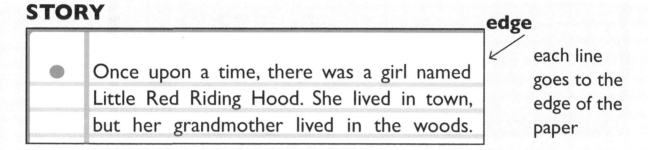

edge

each line goes to the edge of the paper

> ● Once upon a time, there was a girl named Little Red Riding Hood. She lived in town, but her grandmother lived in the woods.

But in a poem, you can "break" a line and end it **before** the edge! Like this:

POEM

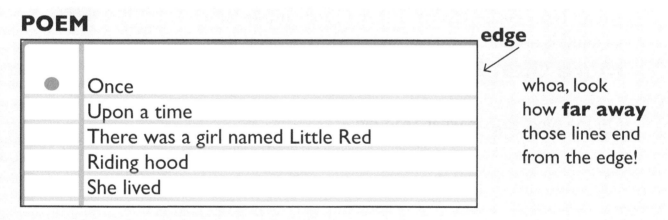

edge

whoa, look how **far away** those lines end from the edge!

> ● Once
> Upon a time
> There was a girl named Little Red
> Riding hood
> She lived

Let's try it! Please **rip out** the 3 lines below, and bring them and your **Poetry Sword** to the next page --

rip here!

I love running across fields

of fresh-cut grass and

sometimes I don't stop.

Got your piece of paper with 3 lines and your poetry sword?

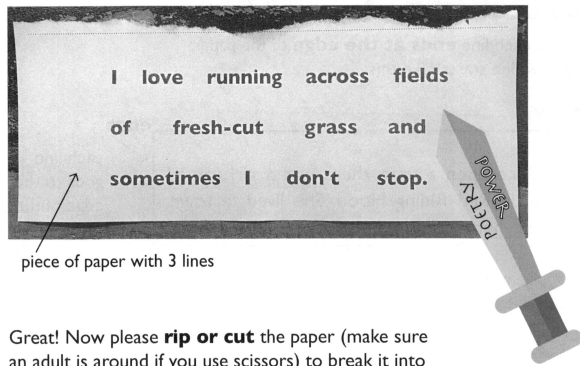

piece of paper with 3 lines

Great! Now please **rip or cut** the paper (make sure an adult is around if you use scissors) to break it into
more than 3 lines!

On the next page is what Sean did...

this part below should be ripped out!

First, Sean decided to rip out the words "I love running" and put them **on their own line**. Like this:

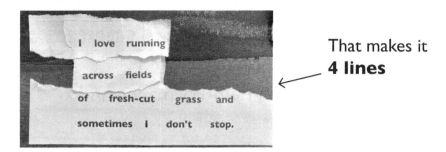

That makes it
4 lines

But you don't have to do what Sean did -- you could break yours into 4 lines, 5, 10, or more! And you can break at **different** places than Sean did. Use your Poetry Sword to help you decide where. Point your sword at a word, and when it feels like a good spot -- **BREAK a line!**

Ok, please give it a try -- **please rip or cut** your paper to break it into more than 3 lines!

LOOK OUT, LINES.

POWER POETRY

There is no wrong place to break a line.

How many lines did you break yours into? Excellent!

> *Tip:* Take a **photo** of your new lines, then re-arrange them again, to try a different combo!

Here's how Sean broke all his lines (the last line is only one word!)

> *Tip:* You can think of each line break as a **pause** when reading a poem.

In poems, you can break lines **anywhere** you want.

Trust your Poetry Sword to guide you. Break a line, or don't! Remember, it's **your** poem.

Sean broke his into 6 lines total

each break is like a pause

The very last line is only one word!

Now that we've broken lines, we're ready to –

chapter video

You've now done a Poem-Formance and two kinds of poems:

> **1. IMAGINE**
> **2. QUESTION**

With this next poem type, you'll earn a **poetry medal!**

poet

To start, please pick one of Amanda's animal paintings on the next page: rabbit or bearded dragon.

Then, like before, **please rip out your animal.**

> # Go ahead -- pick & rip!

rip here!

Hello!
I'm the page on the other side of
the painting of the **rabbit!**

Hello!
I'm the page on the other side of
the painting of the **bearded dragon!**

*Please turn the page, and
bring your animal with you!*

Got your rabbit or bearded dragon?

Great! Please glance at it **super fast,** then look away.

 Now, please look at it again and notice **something new** that you didn't before. Look at it for at least 10 seconds. Use your Artist Monocle if you have it.

Now, please **write** your answers to the questions below about your rabbit or bearded dragon:

What new thing did you notice about it? _____

What do its eyes look like? _____

What sound does it make? _____

What does it smell like? _____

What does its tail feel like? _____

Woot! Excellent job!

You just used four of the **five senses** to describe your rabbit or bearded dragon! (Which one didn't you use? Yup, taste. You could use that one, too, but we decided not to have our animal for dinner.)

Now, even if we took away Amanda's paintings (sorry, Amanda!), we could still "see" the rabbit or bearded dragon with your words alone. We could also hear, smell, and feel it! Doing that -- describing with any of the five senses -- can help paint a picture in your head.

That's called using --

Sensory Details

/ sen-so-ry de-tails /

describing with any of the five senses

Here's part of a poem from *Pet Poems* that uses sensory details:

> ## Toucan
>
> You have time-stretched feathers
> Silky to the touch
> You have moon-bright cheeks
> And shiny-pebble eyes

Those lines use the sensory details of **touch** and **sight**
to help paint a picture of the toucan in our heads.

Now, you try! In the box below, please **write** a poem describing your
rabbit or bearded dragon. Use sensory details to help us paint a picture
of it in our heads. **There are no wrong sensory details.**

Tip #1: You can use the answers you wrote on the last page.
Tip #2: Remember, you can **break** poem lines anywhere you want.

write a poem describing your rabbit or bearded dragon!

Poetry medal!

Please put your name here.

You've earned it!

You've now done **three kinds of poems:**

1. IMAGINE
2. QUESTION
3. DESCRIBE

What is a **DESCRIBE** poem?
It describes an animal,
to paint a picture of it in your head.

You just wrote a DESCRIBE poem on the last page!

And you did it by using **sensory details** to describe the rabbit or bearded dragon, to help paint a picture of it in our heads.

When you do that -- when you paint a picture with words -- the picture can be **vivid**. The more specific or memorable a picture is, the more vivid it is. For example, if you say "**an animal**" in your poem, that paints a slightly vivid picture. If you say "**a snarling snow leopard**," that paints a very vivid one. How vivid should your poem be? That's up to you!

*Let's try some different
levels of vivid —*

First, please pick any animal you want and **write** it in the box below. We picked a penguin. You can pick a penguin, too, or any other animal. **There is no wrong animal to pick.**

Our animal:	*penguin*
Your animal:	

← **write your animal here**

Great choice! Now, let's use different levels of vivid to describe it. Below, we wrote some *slightly vivid* details for how our penguin looks, feels, and sounds. Then, we wrote some **very vivid** details to describe it.

Our penguin:	looks	feels	sounds	
	round	*soft*	*loud*	*slightly vivid*
	portly	**sleek**	**squishy**	**very vivid**

Those give us two different ways to describe our penguin:

> "*Oh penguin – round, soft, and loud.*"
> "*Oh penguin – portly, sleek, and squishy.*"

Which way is **better**? It depends! If we want our poem to paint a very vivid picture, the 2nd is great. If we want less vivid, the 1st is our choice.

Now, you try! Below, please **write** sensory details for how your animal looks, feels, and sounds. Make the top ones slightly vivid, and the bottom very vivid. Remember, the more specific or memorable, the more vivid.

Your animal:	looks	feels	sounds	
write your sensory details here →				slightly vivid
→				**very vivid**

Boom! Now you have two sets of sensory details to paint a picture in our heads. Either can be perfect for your poem. The choice -- as with everything -- is yours!

Sensory details are a great way to paint a mental picture. Another is –

Have you ever heard someone say the sun shines **like** gold?

Using the word "like" is another way to paint a mental picture, by saying what something **reminds you of**. See that pelican's beak below? It reminds us of a slide. Here's how we could show that, using "like":

The pelican's beak is like a slide.

By using "like," we **combined two different things** together, to create a cool picture in our heads. →

Now, you try! In the blank below, please **write** something that the pelican's beak reminds **you** of. Be as weird or strange as you want! *Tip*: It can help to use your Artist Monocle to see what only you can about the pelican's beak. Put whatever you think it's like!

There is no wrong thing that the pelican's beak is like.

The pelican's beak is like _____

Great job! We "like" it!! Hahahahaha get it? Like it? As in...
Okay, sorry, we'll stop with the bad jokes. :)

But we'll never stop with the likes!

Let's create more cool combos —

In the blanks below, please **write** what each thing reminds you of.

For the **hippo**, try and come up with something **no one** has ever thought of before. Use your Artist Monocle if you want. Study it. Be as wild and wacky as you can! **There are no wrong things that each of these are like.**

The squirrel's tail is like _____

The dog's ears are like _____

Go wild with this one!

The hippo is like _____

Awwww yeah, those are amazing!!!

The fancy word for what you just did is --

Simile   **saying what something reminds you of, using "like"**

/ sim-i-le /

By using "like," a simile **combines** two different things to show what they might have in common. And to create a cool mental picture.

So, next time you want a little pizzazz in your poem, add the power of "like!"

Do you <u>have</u> to use "like?" Nope! You can do the same thing with —

Metaphor

saying what something reminds you of, without using "like"

/ met-a-phor /

How can you make a metaphor? Let's find out!

Below are the same three animals from the last page.

In the blanks beside each one, please **write** the **same thing** you did on the last page when you said what each was like.
(If you want, flip back a page to see what you wrote!)

The squirrel's tail is _____

Write the same things
you did on the last page

The dog's ears are _____

Write the same thing here too!

The hippo is _____

BOOM! Now you have a metaphor for each of those!

Maybe earlier you said the squirrel's tail was **like** a sparkler.
Well, now its tail isn't just like a sparkler -- it **is** one!

Remember, in a poem, you can do **anything**.

Let's make more metaphors!

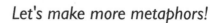

Earlier, we used sensory details to describe a penguin:

> *"Oh penguin – round, soft, and loud."*

We could also use a metaphor to describe it:

> *"Oh penguin, snow rocket!"*

That's a metaphor because it takes one thing (a penguin) and combines it with something the penguin reminds us of (a rocket).

We could also pick something hard to see on its own:

> *"Oh penguin, pure happiness!"*

Happiness can be tough to "see" on its own. But now we have a metaphor to help: happiness looks like a penguin!

Okay, now you try! In the speech bubble below, please **write** what the watermelon reminds you of.

Maybe the watermelon reminds you of a **helmet**. Or something hard to see on its own, like **summer**. Write whatever it reminds you of.

There is no wrong thing to write.

Write what a watermelon reminds you of

Awesome! You just made a metaphor that you could use to describe a watermelon. Maybe like this:

> *"Oh watermelon, **helmet** of juicy protection!"*
> *"The watermelon was **summer**, sticking to my hands."*

Whoa, look at all we've done! In the last few pages, we've described animals (and a watermelon) using metaphors, similes, and sensory details. Each of those can create a really cool picture in our heads. That's called:

Imagery   describing something to create a picture of it in your head

/ im-age-ry /

For many people, what you just did -- using imagery -- is the lifeblood of a poem. **Nice work, poet!**

Okay, ready for a puffin in a hat?

10. Puffins -- and Poets -- Start Your Engines!

 chapter video

We weren't kidding!

What **question** would you like to ask that puffin over there? Please write your question in the box below.

There are no wrong puffin questions.

Your question for the puffin:

```
┌────────────────────────────────────────┐
│                                        │
│                                        │
└────────────────────────────────────────┘
```

Excellent! That's a great way to start a puffin poem!**

**And what <u>kind</u> of poem did you just start? Yup, a QUESTION poem!

Other Ways to Start a Puffin Poem

- Have it **talk** ⟶ *Hello, I'm a hungry puffin*
- Give a **sensory** detail ⟶ *Oh that beak, so pointy*
- Tell what it **reminds** you of ⟶ *Floating like a bubble...*
- Have it **act** ⟶ *Look out! Puffin attack!*
- **However** you want! ⟶ *Ice cream is the best*

Now, you try! Please write one line below to start a new puffin poem. Start it any way you want.

There are no wrong ways to start a poem.

Your new puffin poem start:

```
┌────────────────────────────────────────┐
│                                        │
│                                        │
└────────────────────────────────────────┘
```

Fantastic! You now have two PPPs --
Puffin Poem Possibilities!

*And, after you **start** a poem? Well, then it's time for –*

11. Movin' Middles!

Let's move to the poem **middle** -- its stuffing. (Haha - puffin stuffin'!)

On the next page, please **write** a **question** for the puffin. You can use the same one as before or a new one.

Now, keep it moving! Please **write** two more lines. **There are no wrong lines.** For help, here are --

Ways to Middle a Puffin Poem

- Have the puffin **answer** your question
- Ask it another **question**
- Give a **sensory** detail about the puffin
- Have it **act**
- Or just write **anything you want!**

Got your first three lines? Huzzah! Now, let's --

Drop an elephant!

WHEEE!!!

Please **write** a **few more lines.** And, somewhere in those lines, add an elephant.

- Maybe an elephant **charges** in!
- Maybe the puffin **dreams** it's an elephant
- Maybe the elephant is a new **friend or foe**
- Or anything else!

Just drop an elephant in -- and see what happens! **There is no wrong elephant dropping.**

Puffin question:

▶ chapter video

Two more lines:

A few more lines: (drop an elephant!)

Same puffin question:

Down here: Please **write** the same puffin question you did at the top, to end the poem.

And now –

53

Poetry high-five!

You just wrote an excellent QUESTION poem!

You also did one of our favorite bits of poetry fun -- dropping an elephant.

THAT WAS LOVELY.

Have you ever seen a poem with a **puffin** and an **elephant** before? We haven't!

One of the most powerful things in poetry **is combining different things together,** to make something completely new.

That's what happens when you drop an elephant into your poem -- it creates something probably **no one has ever seen or expected before**. Including you!

 Does it always have to be an elephant?

Absolutely not!

You can drop **anything** into your poem ... person, place, thing, idea ... **acorn**, albatross, accountant ... Australia, acrimony, absolute zero ... anything works!

So, next time you're stuck in a poem?
Drop an elephant!

Or don't!

WHEEE!

(not an elephant)

It's your poem.
You get to choose its path.

Some Poetry Paths

- QUESTION poem
- IMAGINE poem
- DESCRIBE poem
- personification
- ekphrasis
- imagery
- sensory details
- simile
- metaphor
- drop an elephant
- different starts
- different middles

Maybe you'll start a QUESTION poem that also becomes an IMAGINE poem. Can you do that? Sure! It's your poem!

Maybe you'll drop an elephant, add sensory details, or neither!

It's like making **cookies**. You can use a little of this, a lot of that, none of those. Then, make a different cookie -- er, poem -- next time!

delicious poems

For your puffin-elephant poem, we had you end by **repeating** the question you started with. Was that the only way to end it? Nope! There are --

12. Endless Endings!

<u>chapter video</u>

Here's a secret: There is **no right way** to end a poem.

In fact, there are endless ways to end! Here are a few (eight, to be exact) of **our favorites.** We now present you with --

Eight Excellent Endings!

Ending #1 - Repeat the start

For this ending, you **repeat the first line** of your poem. It's a tried-and-true technique that can give a nice sense of coming full circle. And guess what? You've already done it! It's how you ended your puffin-elephant poem a few pages ago.

Okay, to do ending #2, we need a puffin question to start our poems. Ours is below. Please write yours beneath it. You can use one you've done, ask a new one, or use ours. **There is no wrong question.**

Our puffin question:

> *Puffin, what's beneath your hat?*

Your puffin question:

these questions are the same

Great! Now let's –

Ending #2 - Answer the start

On the last page, we started our QUESTION poems with a puffin question. To end those poems, we'll **answer** that question -- like this!

In the two boxes below, we re-wrote our same puffin question, then we wrote an answer to it:

Our puffin question:	*Puffin, what's beneath your hat?*
Our answer:	*Ah yes, that's a lovely place for poems.*

And boom -- we have a poem with a new ending!

? *Can a poem be only* **two lines**? Sure!

Now, you try! Below, please **write** your puffin question from the last page, then please **answer** it. Try and put a different answer than we did if you can. Whatever you put, **there are no wrong answers.**

Your puffin question:	
Your answer:	

Huzzah! You've now done two terrific poem endings!

For the third, imagine your poem's last line is **dangling over a cliff...** Will it fall? Scramble to safety? Get swooped up by a giant pterodactyl?

That kind of ending is a...

Ending #3 – Cliffhanger...

A cliffhanger ending leaves everyone wondering...
WHAT WILL HAPPEN NEXT???

Like this!

Below, we wrote the same puffin question from our last poem. But then we gave it a new ending: a **cliffhanger...**

Our question:	*Puffin, what's beneath your hat?*
Our cliffhanger:	*The hat slowly lifted on its own...*

What's making the hat move? Will something come out from under it? Who knows! A cliffhanger ending keeps you guessing what's next!

Now, you try! Below, please **write** a puffin question. You can use the same one as last time if you want. Then, give it a **cliffhanger** ending -- leave us wondering what happens next! **There are no wrong cliffhangers.**

Your question:	
Your cliffhanger:	

Great job! We're on the edge of our seats!!!

Tip: A cliffhanger ending could also be a question. Like this:

Puffin, what's beneath your hat?
Wait -- did it just move?

Ok, for the next two endings, we need a —

poetry spaceship!

TAKE ME TO YOUR POEMS.

how to build poetry spaceship:

1. find rock

Pick **any rock**! Maybe it's from your yard, or you have one on your shelf. Make sure it's small enough to fit in your palm.

Sean's rock

2. add power

Decorate! Use a pen, markers, paint, stickers, chalk, flowers, whatever you want, to give your rock ultimate travel power.

Sean's poetry spaceship

3. blast off!

Hold the rock in your palm. It is no longer a rock. It now has the power to go **anywhere**. And take you with it! So ... close your fingers around your poetry spaceship, close your eyes, and **imagine where you want to go...**

Ending #4 - Go big!

Imagine you are blasting off in your poetry spaceship, and the puffin is now **far below you,** like a dot on a map.

What do you see near the puffin? A tree? A whole forest? A pirate invasion?

Keep zooming farther out. What else might you see?

That's how you do a go big ending -- put something **bigger than the puffin.**

Here's what we came up with, starting with our same puffin question:

Our question:	*Puffin, what's beneath your hat?*
Our go big:	*Only the stars know.*

Now, you give it a go (big)! Please write a puffin question below (it can be the same as before). Beneath it, please write about something bigger than the puffin. **There are no wrong go big endings.**

Your question:	
Your go big:	

Awesome! A go big ending often leaves you with **a feeling of wonder** or a feeling that **we are all connected**, puffins to people to planets.

Now let's —

Ending #5 - Go small

Imagine your poetry spaceship is zooming back in, getting **closer and closer** to the puffin.

(Your poetry spaceship can go anywhere -- from the edge of the universe to the center of an atom to all the spaces in-between.)

As you zoom in, what do you see? The fine filaments of its feathers? The tiny chip in its beak? The thoughts flying inside its puffin head?

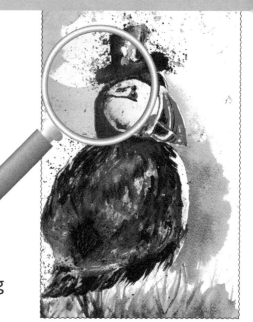

That's how you do a go small ending -- put something **smaller than the puffin.**

Here's what we came up with, starting with our same puffin question:

Our question:	*Puffin, what's beneath your hat?*
Our go small:	*Just a single thought.*

Now, you give it a go (small). Please **write** a puffin question below (it can be the same as before). Beneath that, please write about something **smaller** than the puffin. **There are no wrong go small endings.**

Your question:	
Your go small:	

Great job! A go small ending often leaves you with **a feeling of calm,** comfort, or quiet.

You can also end with a --

Ending #6 - Twist

Please take another look at the puffin.

What's something **surprising** about it, that only you can see? (*Tip*: Your Artist Monocle might help here.)

Maybe it has a battalion of warrior birds! Maybe it's a magic puffin. Maybe it's not a puffin at all...

That's how you do a twist ending -- reveal a **surprise about the puffin.**

Here's what we came up with, starting with our same puffin question:

Our question:	*Puffin, what's beneath your hat?*
Our twist:	*The hat opened, and we climbed in.*

Now, you try! Please write a puffin question below (it can be the same as before). Beneath it, please put something surprising about the puffin. **There are no wrong twist endings.**

Your question:	
Your twist:	

Whoa, we didn't see that coming -- great job!!
A twist is an **exciting** way to finish a poem!

Okay, for the next ending (only 2 left!), we need to --

62

Find Your Poet's Heart

Please look around the place you are in. What do you see that makes you smile? Or frown? Pick one thing. **There is no wrong choice.**

If you don't see anything where you are, think about something **important** to you: an object or person or place. It could also be a memory. Pick one thing. **There is no wrong choice.**

Whatever you picked, please **write** it on a small strip of paper. It might be one word, two words, a whole sentence. You could also draw it.

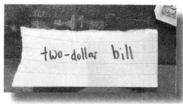

what Sean picked

Now, please fold up your paper. How does what you wrote inside it make you **feel**? Happy? Sad? Scared? Excited?

Whatever emotion you feel, please **write** it on the folded paper. It could be more than one. If you're not sure if something is an emotion, go ahead and include it. **There are no wrong emotions.**

how it makes Sean feel

Lastly, please turn over your folded paper and **draw** a heart. **This is your poet's heart.**

Sean's poet's heart

If you want, tape up the paper so it doesn't unfold. Now, please bring your poet's heart and let's end a poem --

Ending #7 - With feeling

Has a poem or book ever made you cry? Or laugh? Or feel like you belong?

That's how you do an ending with feeling -- try to make us feel an **emotion** in the line you write.

Here's the feeling line we came up with, starting with our same puffin question:

Our question:	*Puffin, what's beneath your hat?*
Our feeling line:	*Who cares -- we're just glad you're here.*

We wrote our feeling line with the emotion of feeling **grateful.**

Now, you try. First, please **write** a puffin question in the box below (it can be the same as before). Before you write in the next box, please --

hold your poet's heart in your hand

-- and **pick an emotion**. It can be one written on your poet's heart, or any other. You might choose joy, sadness, anger, calm, or any other feeling.

In the bottom box, please **write** a feeling line with that emotion.

There is no wrong emotion and no wrong feeling line.

Your question:	
Your feeling line:	

Thank you for that ending. For many people, how a
poem makes you feel is **the most important part.** *Now we'll end with –*

Ending #8 - Whatever you want!

You just practiced seven (7!!) tried-and-true ways to end poems. Are those the only ways? No way!

There's an **infinity** of ways to end a poem!

Including perhaps the best way -- end with **whatever** you want. After all, it's your poem!

Below, we started with our same puffin question, then came up with a whatever ending.

Our question:	*Puffin, what's beneath your hat?*
Our whatever:	*Ice cream is the best.*

Does that mean there's ice cream under the puffin's hat? Who knows! Poems often **leave it up to the reader** to decide what they mean. We just went with the first thing that popped out of our head!

Now, you try! Please **write** a puffin question below. (It can be the same as before.)

Beneath it, put **whatever** you want! If you're stuck, go with the first thing that pops out of your head! It doesn't have to be about the puffin at all.

There are no wrong whatever endings.

Your question:	
Your whatever:	

Whoa, we love it!

your poetry arsenal!

Here's what you've acquired so far --

IMAGINE poems
QUESTION poems
DESCRIBE poems

PERSONIFICATION   **SIMILE**

EKPHRASIS   **METAPHOR**

SENSORY DETAILS   **IMAGERY**

poetry sword
(for confidence)
(and breaking lines)

Artist Monocle
(to see what only you can)

poet's heart
(for emotion)

poetry spaceship
(to travel anywhere)

STRONG STARTS

- ask a question
- have the animal talk
- give a sensory detail
- tell what the animal reminds you of
- have it act
- whatever you want!

MOVIN' MIDDLES

- answer a question
- ask another question
- add a sensory detail
- action
- drop an elephant
- whatever you want!

ENDLESS ENDINGS

- repeat the start
- answer the start
- cliffhanger...
- go BIG!
- go small
- twist
- with feeling
- whatever you want!

You're now fully equipped for poetry —

13. Funtimes!

chapter video

Please pick **any** animal on this page.
(No need to cut or rip it out!)

Got your animal? Great!

Now, please **write** a poem about it!

Use anything from your poetry arsenal!

Play! Experiment! **Have fun!**

Poem!

Woo-hoo, amazing job!!!

Try a Poem-Formance of it!!

Send us your poem: poems@PetPoemsPlus.com
(get permission from a parent or teacher first),
and we may post it on our website!

Your poetry arsenal is now totally 100% complete, right?
Hmm... Maybe, possibly, there's room for...

14. Repetition
Repetition
Repetition

Take a look at this **goat**.

In the box below, please **write**
the first line for a poem about it.

You might ask it a question, describe it, imagine what it would say, use your Artist Monocle or poet's heart or poetry spaceship to zoom in or out, or do whatever you want! **There is no wrong first line.**

first line:

Great! Now, in this box, please **repeat** that same line:

repeat it:

Double great! Can you repeat a line in a poem? Double yes!

Repetition is one of the most popular pieces of poetry treasure!

Now, please **write** a new line below, that is different from your first line. Put whatever you want! **There is no wrong new line.**
Then, in the last box, please **write** your first line again.

new line:

first line:

Hip-hip huzzah! With those 4 lines, you wrote a great **goat poem!**
70 Is it okay that 3 lines are the same? Sure! That's repetition!

Here's the goat poem we came up with, doing the same thing as you on the last page. Just like yours, ours repeats a line 3 times (in orange):

our goat poem

> I am perched on the edge
> I am perched on the edge
> What comes next?
> I am perched on the edge!

Is a **line** the only thing you can repeat?

Not in the least least least! You can repeat **anything** in a poem:

> - line
> - phrase
> - word
> - letter
> - image
> - sound

A phrase is a few words, but not an entire line.
How could you repeat a phrase in a poem? Like this!

our goat poem #2

> I will stand at the edge
> I will dream the world...
> What comes next?
> I will head-butt fear.

Boom! That poem repeats the phrase "I will" 3 times (in green).
Have you ever heard lines or phrases repeated **in a song?**
Just like in a song, repetition can give your poem rhythm.   *Because --*

Poetry is like music.

You know how songs can make you tap your foot, bob your head, even get up and dance? That's because the song has **rhythm**.

Poems can do the same thing with repetition!

Poems & Songs

- have rhythm
- make you feel something
- aren't too long

Some poet-scholars argue that repetition is what sets poetry apart from an essay or story.

But we don't want to argue! We want to find more ways to --

make your poem sing with repetition!

Remember, you can repeat anything --

- **line**
- phrase
- word
- **letter**
- **image**
- sound

Let's see how you might repeat a word and a **letter**!

This poem repeats the word **edge**:

> I will stand at the edge
> The edge of fear
> Edge? There is no edge...

This poem repeats **starting** letters:

> I lean at the ledge
> What world awaits?
> Daring, daunting, dreams...

Look at all that lovely repetition! Now, you try!
Please **write** a line in each box below.
The lines can be part of the above poems, or not!
There are no wrong lines.

a line with the word **edge** in it:

a line that repeats **starting** letters:

Excellent! Btw? When you repeated those starting letters? You also did --

AMAZING
AWESOME
ALLITERATION!

alliteration
/ al-lit-er-a-tion /

when words close together
start **with the same letter**

What else can we repeat?

repeating an image

Remember when we added imagery to a poem?
Imagery is describing something to paint a picture of it in your head.

Earlier, we described a penguin with this metaphor:

> Oh penguin, snow rocket!

That gives us an **image** of a penguin as a rocket. Now, we could repeat that same line, or a word or phrase from it, all of which could be great.

But we could also repeat the image of our rocket penguin using **different words** than we did before. Like this:

> Oh penguin, snow **rocket**!
> Waddling back and forth
> Picking up speed and --
> **Blast off**! Due north!

The last line repeats the **image** of our penguin rocket with all new words, by having it blast off, which is something a **rocket** does.

Now, you try! Think of **something else** a rocket does. Maybe it flies through space, or lands on the moon, or anything else!

Now, please use that to ᴡʀɪᴛᴇ a line where a **penguin acts like a rocket:**

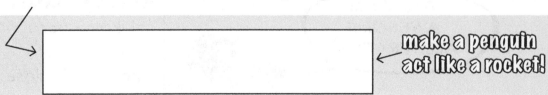

make a penguin
act like a rocket!

Aw yeah, go go penguin rocket! **Using new words** to describe an image you've already used is a brilliant form of repetition! Another is --

repeating a sound

A super fun thing to do in your poems is repeat how a word **sounds**.
Like in this one from *Pet Poems* --

My Secret!

Ahahaha
I have it **here!**
Yes yes yes
My precious **dear!**

That poem repeats the sound of the last words (the ones **in purple**) in the
second and fourth lines. That kind of repetition is known as --

rhyming!

Now, you try! In the box below, we started a rhyming
poem about that dog over there. Please help us finish.

At the end of the last line, please **write** something that
rhymes with **please** in the blank space.

It doesn't have to make sense or rhyme perfectly --
anything is fine! **There is no wrong rhyme.**

I'm a good dog
I always say **please**
I love everything!
Except for _____ ← **your rhyme**

Excellent! That was a prime-time rhyme sublime!

If you like rhymes, here
are two of our best -- 75

rhyming tips & tricks

1. Look it up!

Did you know there are rhyming dictionaries?

So, if you want a rhyme for "goat" (or anything), look it up!

Tip: You can also search for words that **almost** rhyme.

"What almost rhymes with **goat**?"

2. Set up a sloth! (part one)

This is one of Sean's favorite rhyming tricks!

To start, think of a fun thing **for this sloth to say.** Maybe it says what it ate for lunch. Maybe it shares its big slothy dreams. Or anything else! In the box below, we wrote our sloth saying -- what we think it would say.

Please **write** your sloth saying beneath it. You can use ours if you want or put anything else! **There is no wrong sloth saying.**

Our sloth saying: *I can reach the moon!*

Your sloth saying:

Great! And now –

2. Set up a sloth! (part two)

Below, we wrote the **end word** from our sloth saying ("*moon*").
Please do the same -- please write your sloth saying end word below.

Our end word:

moon

Your end word:

Great! Below, we put a word that **rhymes** with our end word (we chose "**soon**"). Please do the same. Below, please write a word that rhymes with your end word. **There is no wrong rhyme word.**

Our rhyme word:

soon

Your rhyme word:

Nice! Now, let's use that to **set up our sloth**! Below, we wrote a 4-line poem. Line 2 ends with our rhyme word ("**soon**"). That sets up the poem to end with our sloth saying on line 4 -- and to rhyme!

Now, you try! Below, please write a 4-line poem and:
- end line 2 with your rhyme word
- make line 4 be your sloth saying

Play around! Have fun! **There is no wrong poem.**

Our poem:
1 *Maybe not today*
2 *Maybe not too soon*
3 *I may not be fast but*
4 *I can reach the moon!*

Your poem:
1
2
3
4

these lines are the same →

*Sloth-tastic!
Now let's --*

What's your favorite song?

Does the music have a **beat** to it? Something that makes you want to snap or sway? Maybe it's **drums** or bass, guitar or keyboard, violin or ukulele.

That's the **rhythm** of the music.

rhythm

/ rhy-thm /

a strong repeated pattern of sound

Poems often have rhythm, too, because:

Poems are word music.

Lots of poems have a rhythm that switches between **STRONG** and **light** beats. Like when a drumbeat in a song goes **BOOMba BOOMba BOOM**!

That's what happened in our sloth poem from the last page!

MAYbe NOT toDAY
MAYbe NOT too SOON
I may NOT be FAST but
I can REACH the MOON!

CAN you ... HEAR the ... BEAT?

Tip: Reading a poem out loud can be a great way to hear its beats and rhythm.

Ready? Let's –

lay down some poetry beats!

In the box below, we started a poem about those jellyfish, using the **BOOMba BOOMba BOOM** beat.

Please help us finish it! Beneath our lines, please **write** one more. Try to make yours have the **BOOMba BOOMba BOOM** beat.

Tip: Saying it out loud can help. Just give it your best jellyfish try!

There is no wrong BOOMba beat line.

your BOOMba beat line →

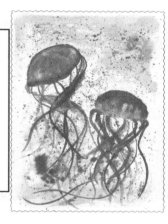

> **WE** have **DEEP** sea **FUN**
> **WE** have **DEEP** sea **GLOW**
> **WE** can **DANCE** real **FAST**

Awwww yeah! We are dancing to your BOOMba beat!

The BOOMba beat is just one poetry rhythm. You could do the opposite and have the beat go **baBOOM baBOOM baBOOM** -- like this!

> to**DAY** I **GO** to **SCHOOL**
> to**MOR**row I'll be **COOL**

Or come up with your own rhythm. Or have no rhythm at all!

Remember, in poetry, **there are no rules.**

To hear some great rhythm & rhyme & repetition poems, try:

- Amanda Gorman
- Nikki Giovanni
- Shel Silverstein
- "When Dawn Comes to the City" by Claude McKay
- "Annabel Lee" by Edgar Allan Poe

Now it's –

chapter video

So far, we've done three kinds of poems about pets (also not just pets):

> **IMAGINE** -- the animal talks to us
> **QUESTION** -- we talk to it
> **DESCRIBE** -- we paint a picture of it with words

Now, let's do a fourth kind of poem:

> **STORY** -- we learn the animal's story

Here's the start of a STORY poem about a rhino from *Pet Poems:*

Why-No-Sir

I will tell you my story
Sad but true
I will tell it but once
And only to you

The rest of that poem (it's a long one!) tells that rhino's story.

Now, you try! Below, please **write** two lines to **start** a STORY poem about that deer. Maybe the deer just woke up. Maybe we're about to find out how it got its superpower. **There are no wrong ways to start a STORY poem.**

two lines about the deer

*Excellent! Now let's turn your
STORY poem start into —*

Where will your deer STORY poem go next? Let's find out!

In the box below, please **write** your answers to the questions about your deer's story. You can put whatever you want! **There are no wrong deer answers.**

In your deer's story --

What happens next? _____

Who does the deer meet? _____

What problem do they face? _____

How do they solve it? _____

How does this story end? _____

Boom! Now you've got all the ingredients both for a great STORY poem -- and a great **play!** To stage the play, you might:

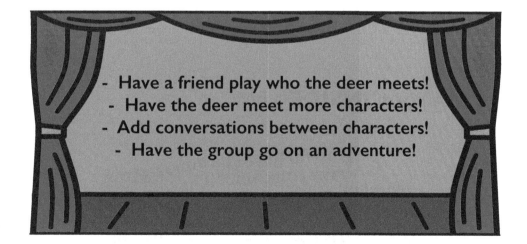

- Have a friend play who the deer meets!
- Have the deer meet more characters!
- Add conversations between characters!
- Have the group go on an adventure!

Then ... find some props ... gather an audience ... get the performers in their starting positions, and ... **act out your deer play!**

Not only can you act out a poem, you can –

In poetry, you can be a rebel...

All poems have to be done in straight lines, right?

NOPE!

You could wrap a poem **AROUND** a lizard --

I am alone, happy and elated A fly was here too... But I just ate it.

You could put a poem **INSIDE** a bear --

How far have you gone? How far have you come? I have walked, padded, traipsed, fields and forests mists and mountains, lands and light years. All travelers wear a bit of their past, and future. Where have you been? Where, oh where, will you go next?

Give it a try!

Below, please write a poem **around** the pelican and a poem **inside** the dog.

They could be IMAGINE poems, DESCRIBE poems, STORY poems, QUESTION poems, or anything!

There is no wrong poem.

Put a poem
AROUND the
pelican

Put a poem
INSIDE the
dog

Excellent poem-drawing!
Need ideas for what to do next?
Here are some ways for –

18. Getting Help

We all get stuck sometimes! Here are some books and online tools for poetry help.

chapter video

"What's another word for **bold**?"

With a **thesaurus**, you look up one word and it gives different words that mean the same thing. It's a great way to add variety to your poems!

"What rhymes with **bold**?"

With a **rhyming dictionary**, you look up one word and it gives you different words that sound the same. It's a big help for rhyming poems!

Other tools can help as well. You can even ask some for a whole poem:

> write me a poem about a bold sloth

Which can be really fun, but since you aren't the only one writing it --

it wouldn't truly be YOUR poem.

Instead of using those online tools or programs to write the **whole** poem, there are some really cool ways they can help with **parts** of it!

They might help you get **ideas** for --

> - similes and metaphors
> - sensory details
> - questions for a QUESTION poem
> - whatever else you can think of!

Let's see how!

Getting simile & metaphor ideas

Remember, a simile or metaphor shows what two different things might have in common. So, let's say you've got a **sloth** in your poem. (Hi, slothy!) You might use online tools to get simile and metaphor ideas by asking --

- What is it like?
- What does it have in common with something else?

> what is a sloth like?

> what do sloths and slides have in common?

Those aren't the only searches -- you can try tons of different ones! And whatever suggestions the books or tools give, it's still up to you to decide if you **want** to use them. And **how** to work them into YOUR poem.

Getting sensory details & question ideas

You can use online tools to get ideas for other things, too!

> what are some sensory details for a sloth?

> what questions could you ask a sloth?

I AM NOT A COMPUTER!

Remember, **you** get to choose what to use and how. Because **no one** sees the world exactly like you do -- not even a mega-powered supercomputer!

Let's wrap up with --

19. Revision

chapter video

You have assembled a formidable fantastic poetry arsenal!

Now, let's look at **revision** -- stuff you might try once you've written a poem and want to make it even better.

HIII-YAH! LET'S SLICE UP SOME POEMS!

Change the title

Here's a small change that can make a big difference. Read your poem and pick a word or phrase that **jumps out** at you. Now, try using that word or phrase as the **new title** of your poem!

Here's another: When you read your poem, how does it make you feel? Try using that **emotion** as the poem's title.

Changing the title can be a fun way to add new depth to your poem!

End earlier

Is there a line in your poem that makes you chuckle? Or that tugs at your poet's heart? Try ending the poem early, by making that line the **last** one. (To do that, just delete all the lines after it.)

Ending on a funny or emotional line can leave a lasting impression. And it's fine if that makes the poem shorter -- short poems are great, too!

Harvest a new poem

Is there a word or phrase in your poem that you **really** like? Try writing a whole new poem with that word or phrase as the title!

Maybe your poem has the words "penguin relish" in it and you love that phrase. Try writing a new poem called Penguin Relish!

your poetry arsenal!

simile
metaphor
imagery

QUESTION poems
DESCRIBE poems
IMAGINE poems
STORY poems

repetition
alliteration

personification
sensory details

rhyme
rhythm

I FEAR NO WORD!

Sprinkle in something new

Is there anything you might add to the poem?

Take a look at your **poetry arsenal** for ideas. Maybe add a bit of repetition, alliteration, or rhythm. Or scatter in some sensory detail, the power of "like," or use your poet's heart to add emotion. Try traveling in your poetry spaceship for a new perspective, or using your Artist Monocle to see your poem the way only YOU can. Or, of course, drop an elephant!

Take out stuff you don't like

Instead of adding, are there words or lines in your poem that just don't quite seem to fit? Try taking them out of the poem. *Tip*: "I fear no word!" means not being afraid to **remove** words!

Move stuff around

Here's a fun revision technique to try! First, take your poem and tear or cut out** each line, so that each is on its own piece of paper. Then, try shuffling the lines around, like puzzle pieces. Maybe you'll like it even more with the lines in new places!

**always make sure an adult is around when you use scissors

And now some parting –   87

20. Advice for Poets

chapter video

In this book, you've written tons of poems and added all sorts of power to your poetry arsenal. We now proclaim you an --

Officially Certified Poet (OCP)

Please fill in the Certificate on the other page. Write your name in the box. You can keep your Certificate in this book or tear it out and put it anywhere -- your desk, your mirror, in a frame, folded up in your pocket or backpack, wherever! If you mess up don't worry -- there's another Certificate at the back of this book and more at www.PetPoemsPlus.com.

And now, Officially Certified Poet (OCP), here are our top two pieces of advice as you continue on your poetry path --

Fill Your Poetry Well

Each week, pick **one new thing to learn about**. If you like astronomy, go look up binary stars or red giants or dark matter. If you're into animals, find out more about ptarmigans, pangolins, or the common snail. Discover how rivers change course, why oak trees spread out and pine trees shoot straight up. Pick one new thing each week, and fill your poetry well! Then, you can dip into that well for new poem ideas. Also, when you're not looking, the new stuff often seeps into your poems in really cool ways.

Write Everyday

How does a good soccer player become great? How does a decent drummer become a superstar? How does a good cook become a world-class chef? **They practice.** Nearly every day, they play a little soccer, drum for at least a few minutes, make one omelette. Poetry is the same. The best way to get better is to exercise your poetry muscles. It doesn't have to be a lot -- just make the time to write one line each day, and you'll be amazed at how much you improve.

And now, OCP -- go forth, and poem!

Be it known to all --

Certificate

That on this ___ day of the month of _____
in the year _____, award-winning professional poet Sean
Petrie and award-winning professional artist Amanda
Hoxworth, do hereby declare that --

is now and for all days henceforth an --

Officially Certified Poet (OCP)

Said OCP has completed the rigorous training of the *Pet
Poems Plus* coursebook, as well as crafted a poetry arsenal
that includes the formidable Poetry Sword, the passionate
Poet's Heart, the adventurous Poetry Spaceship, and the all-
seeing Artist Monocle, as well achieving proficiency in several
powerful poetry skills, including repetition, alliteration,
personification, imagery, sensory details, the power of "like"
(simile), metaphor, rhythm, rhyme, and dropping an elephant.

Said OCP is also approved for writing all poem types,
including Imagine, Question, Describe, and Story poems.

Wherefore, said OCP shall now bear all the official rights and
duties attached thereto, including unlimited use of the title
POET, writing poems whenever and wherever they please,
sharing their work with others, and, above all, having fun
in the art and practice of poetry.

Sean Petrie

Amanda Hoxworth

OFFICIALLY
POET™
CERTIFIED

Extra Pages

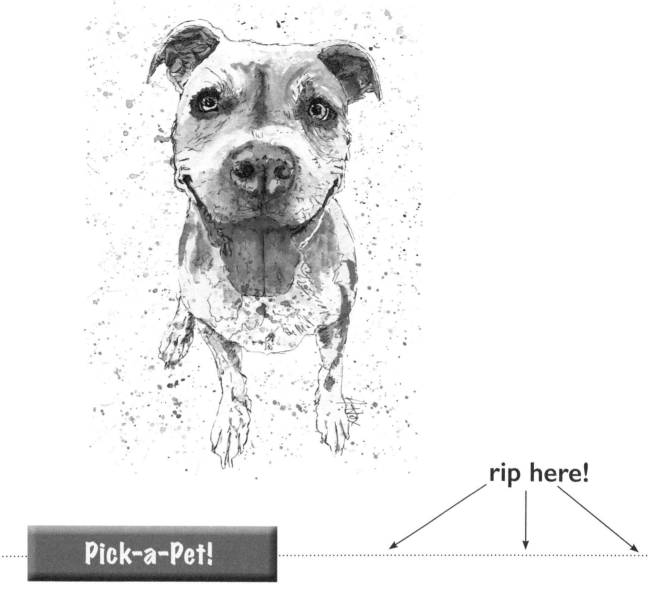

rip here!

Pick-a-Pet!

Hello!
I'm the page on the other side
of the **dog!**

Hello!
I'm the page on the other side
of the **cat!**

I love running across fields

of fresh-cut grass and

sometimes I don't stop.

rip here!

I love running across fields

of fresh-cut grass and

sometimes I don't stop.

I love running across fields

of fresh-cut grass and

94

sometimes I don't stop.

ARTIST MONOCLE **INSTRUCTIONS**

Step 1: More ripping! **Rip out** the bottom half of this page.

Step 2: **Carefully cut** around the dashed lines.
When you use scissors, make sure an adult is around.
Make a hole in the gray center part.
<u>Hint:</u> Poking the center with a pencil might help.

Step 3: **Decorate** your Monocle! Use markers, stickers, whatever!

rip here

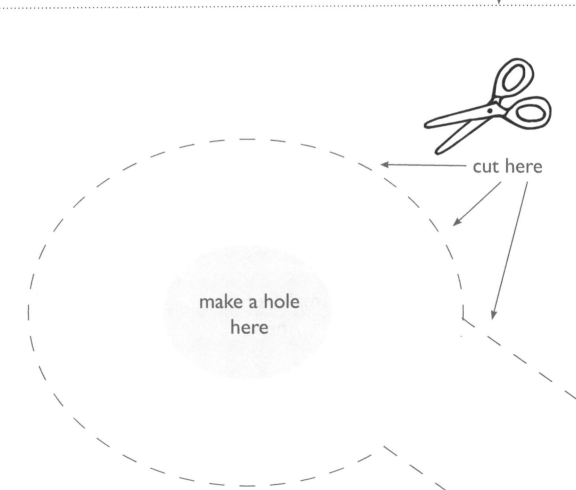

cut here

make a hole
here

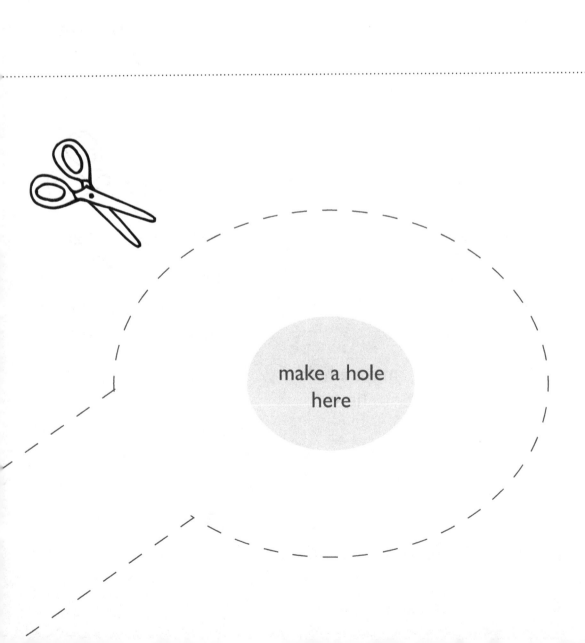

make a hole
here

rip here!

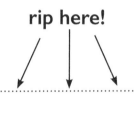

Make Some Sense

Hello!
I'm the page on the other side of the **rabbit!**

Hello!
I'm the page on the other side of the **bearded dragon!**

your poetry arsenal!

I FEAR NO WORD!

poems

IMAGINE poems
QUESTION poems
DESCRIBE poems
STORY poems

IMAGERY	REPETITION
METAPHOR	ALLITERATION
SIMILE	RHYME
SENSORY DETAILS	RHYTHM
PERSONIFICATION	EKPHRASIS

poetry sword
(for confidence)
(and breaking lines)

Artist Monocle
(to see what only you can)

poet's heart
(for emotion)

poetry spaceship
(to travel anywhere)

STRONG STARTS

- ask a question
- have the animal talk
- give a sensory detail
- tell what the animal reminds you of
- have it act
- whatever you want!

MOVIN' MIDDLES

- answer a question
- ask another question
- add a sensory detail
- action
- drop an elephant
- whatever you want!

ENDLESS ENDINGS

- repeat the start
- answer the start
- cliffhanger...
- go BIG!
- go small
- twist
- with feeling
- whatever you want!

Be it known to all --

Certificate

That on this ___ day of the month of _____
in the year _____, award-winning professional poet Sean
Petrie and award-winning professional artist Amanda
Hoxworth, do hereby declare that --

is now and for all days henceforth an --

Officially Certified Poet (OCP)

Said OCP has completed the rigorous training of the *Pet
Poems Plus* coursebook, as well as crafted a poetry arsenal
that includes the formidable Poetry Sword, the passionate
Poet's Heart, the adventurous Poetry Spaceship, and the all-
seeing Artist Monocle, as well achieving proficiency in several
powerful poetry skills, including repetition, alliteration,
personification, imagery, sensory details, the power of "like"
(simile), metaphor, rhythm, rhyme, and dropping an elephant.

Said OCP is also approved for writing all poem types,
including Imagine, Question, Describe, and Story poems.

Wherefore, said OCP shall now bear all the official rights and
duties attached thereto, including unlimited use of the title
POET, writing poems whenever and wherever they please,
sharing their work with others, and, above all, having fun
in the art and practice of poetry.

Sean Petrie

Amanda Hoxworth

OFFICIALLY
POET™
CERTIFIED

BURLWOOD BOOKS

Austin, Texas
BurlwoodBooks.com

First published in the United States of America
by Burlwood Books 2023

ISBN 979-8-9850784-4-2

1. Creative Writing—Poetry 2. Pets—Poetry 3. Animals—Poetry
4. Human-animal relationships—Poetry

fish (splash)

What is it like to breath underwater?

What is it like to live underwater?

What is it like to only be able to swim and not walk?

What human food would you like to eat?

fish, fish, fish

Made in the USA
Monee, IL
21 October 2023